The Healing Garden

The Healing Garden

by MARJORIE HARRIS

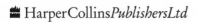
HarperCollins*PublishersLtd*

for Jennifer

http://www.harpercollins.com

First edition

Canadian Cataloguing in Publication Data

Harris, Marjorie
 The healing garden

ISBN 0-00-255432-1

1. Gardening - Therapeutic use.   2. Gardens - Psychological aspects.   I. Title.

RM735.7.G37H37 1996   615.8'515   C95-933310-X

96 97 98 99 v EB 10 9 8 7 6 5 4 3 2 1

Printed and bound in the United States

Design: Joseph Gisini / Andrew Smith Graphics Inc.

Contents

Acknowledgements

Even a small book takes a lot of work and I had plenty of help. Thanks to: my daughter Jennifer Harris for splendid research; horticultural therapist Karen York for tracking down books and people; Bond Strand, who took me canoeing and shared so generously his information about Native healing practices; Jan Watkins, whose life and thoughts are overwhelming in their courage; Sheree Lee Olson, who read the manuscript; and especially to Iris Tupholme—the book was her idea—and Jocelyn Laurence, who is a terrific editor.

Introduction

The garden heals. We hear these words and recognize they are true. Those of us who garden see what we do as creating a sanctuary from the forces of darkness, within and without. A haven of serenity, a respite from the noisy civilization around us.

IT IS THROUGH the mythic search for the rejuvenation of one's soul that we discover the healing garden. In some way, we all need to recognize our place within nature. We echo nature because we are a part of it. But we are also beginning to be aware that gardens have a much more powerful hold over humans than we had previously imagined. Our curiosity about how we relate to nature means we have begun to study the natural world around us with great intensity, revealing a seemingly endless number of astonishing discoveries.

We shouldn't be so surprised, though, at the intimate link between ourselves and growing things. Our bodies offer a parallel to the biological structure of plants in several ways. We both have a vascular system (our blood, their sap); they are affected by the pull of the moon, as are not only the tides but the movement of cytoplasm in our own bodies; we, too, respond to warmth and cold. We are dependent on water. When we think of plants, we feel empathy.

HOW WE GO gently into decay endlessly fascinates gardeners. I sometimes meditate on the miracle of renewal in observing something as simple as the immense forces at work in compost. I wonder how minute creatures can, out of dead and dying detritus, manufacture such extraordinary, life-giving material as humus. And it leads me to ponder: Where will my own body go?

THE GARDEN REFUSES to leave me alone. The great nature writer Barry Lopez says that the purpose and order of our interior landscape are dependent on where we live, the patterns we observe in nature, our life on the land—even in cities. "The interior landscape," he writes in *Arctic Dreams*, "responds to the character and subtlety of an exterior landscape; the shape of the individual mind is as affected by land as it is by genes."

I know I've changed—in some intricate way—with each new place I've lived. The way the wind blows, what kind of sights I see, the colours of the world around me all affect who I am at that moment. Since I first started gardening, I have been aware how much this has influenced the rest of my life. I went from being a nervous, driven person to someone who could sit and meditate; from being restless and depressed to becoming strong and useful in my surroundings.

Before I took up gardening, I used to go to a massage therapist to unravel the twists of my mind and body. I would lie naked with my head in this woman's hands and give myself up to her healing touch. This was a new idea to me.

So was the concept of being able to trust someone else so completely and to reveal all—in other words, to give myself over to the Other. How often can any of us do this? We hang onto our selves, often with something close to desperation. Keep it in, stay in control. That Other—in my case the garden, which is nature itself—is readily available. But the garden heals only if we allow it to do so, and not until it's possible to give ourselves up freely.

The garden has taught me how to unleash myself. It came sneaking up on me slowly, insinuating itself in a mysterious way into my life. The more the garden demanded of me, the more I seemed to need it. We were forming a symbiosis whose effectiveness I'm only beginning to understand.

MY GARDEN is not a hobby. It is a fascination, an amazement. It is, occasionally, an obsession. What else do I really want to think about? When I make the transition into the garden—stepping across the deck, dodging the mess that seems perpetually to lie about—I'm conscious of a feeling of expectation. Something will happen here. When my stomach roils, work becomes impossible and the world has gone mad, I know I must go into the garden to destroy a few bugs, stir up the compost, break fallen branches into small pieces.

I fling myself outside in anger only to find I am absorbed by this Other that I rely on implicitly. I may have started out to pull a weed, absorb a scent or sit, briefly, and feel the sun on my body. But, whether I'm conscious of it or not, I'm here to be rescued. It is this same sense of need that affects people who are ill—this ability nature has of distracting us from ourselves, making us forget who and what we are by drawing us away from whatever troubles the world presents.

As a bee moves about the intense blue blossoms of the caryopteris, I am dazzled by its swift movements. The wings of this creature beat madly to keep it in place as it extracts the life-giving nectar from impossibly tiny flowers. This is a miracle, however small. How does the bee perform this demanding task with leg pouches so swollen they threaten to drag it earthward? Why doesn't it go home now? My recovery begins.

This is the essence of the healing garden—the ability to lift us beyond the presence of mere ego. The "I" in me no longer exists. I am thrilled with the scent of the flowers, enchanted by the busyness of insects. A butterfly really does land on the butterfly bush, bobbing up and down like a small ship at sea as the soft autumn breeze gently moves the branches. The only thought that intrudes is: Where do butterflies sleep at night? It sends me into the house to read about butterflies. All else becomes irrelevant until I find that they roost under leaves, blending in with the landscape so successfully we never see them after dusk.

WHAT IS IT about the garden that makes it such a place of healing? Perhaps we project hope into it each time we set foot into this place. "How wonderful this new plant will be next season when it comes into its own," we think. How truly amazing that anything will survive because it is too cold or too hot, or there is too much or too little rain. And yet survive it does.

It is impossible to be weary of life here. There is far too much to be done. Even in the dead of winter, mulching goes on. Summer or winter, something has to be picked up, reorganized or dug into physically, or, when all else fails, there are magazines to be read and plans for the future to be made on scraps of paper.

The mind is worked, but so is the body. Our instinct for pleasure leads us to enjoy the humble act of digging in the soil or getting our hands dirty. But intellectual content is also important. You can't garden without deliberation and study. There is always something to learn from a book or from a person who is far more expert than you are. You become clearer in your thinking, about the garden and thus about life. A garden slows you down long enough to make connections that can bring a much fuller, more sensual existence.

WHENEVER I COME into the garden I am determined not to spend all my time here. I should do the laundry. Nothing, however, seems quite as important as spreading mulch, even though the day is windy and cold. It takes a painfully long time, but the sense of exhilaration with this kind of hard labour is indescribable. All the cobwebs are swept away. My logy body is refreshed.

Afterward, I want a hot drink and a good stare at what is, to my no-longer-jaded eyes, a scene filled with heart-stopping beauty, even though the garden has been stripped of all bloom except the very last, undaunted, shadowy blue monkshood. For this moment, the berries on all the shrubs and vines have not been scavenged by hungry birds. They stand out like the art nouveau grilles in a Paris metro.

WHY DO WE derive so much pleasure from nature? The most obvious reason is because it is where we come from and where we return. But we've managed to objectify it so completely that we often lose sight of the fact that we are one with nature. We've developed a whole culture that tries its best to subdue nature rather than live within it.

But when we are sick—sometimes in mind, sometimes in body—we flee to the garden to make ourselves better. As we step away from the rigid concrete into the silent forest, perhaps the atavistic past lurking in our genes tells us we've come home. We're in the natural place for us to be.

Henry David Thoreau told us that not only is nature our limit and measure, but the world can be revealed in our back yard if we give it a chance. Perhaps that's what I'm looking for—revelation. I know I am a part of this place like no other, and that it reflects me and what I am.

The garden is the only place I'm confident that I can see properly into the heart of things. I look intensely at each plant, my eyes darting about, picking up a small combination of colours here, a chewed-up leaf there. All of it must be minutely examined. I smell the roots, caress the leaves and sniff the air constantly like some alert animal. I am alert, much more so than I normally am. I am infused with a kind of supersensitivity.

My spiritual and physical life are completely entwined with the garden. It's a nourishing wellspring of energy and strength. It impels me on into the future. It is here I do my worshipping.

RIGHT: *A brief moment in the wilderness of Bon Echo Park just as the first travellers must have seen it.* (PHOTOGRAPH BY MARJORIE HARRIS)

OVERLEAF: *My own garden in the middle of the city is as much a retreat as it is a pleasure to work in.* (PHOTOGRAPH BY MARJORIE HARRIS)

The First Garden:
The Wilderness

It is easy to understand why one of the central myths of creation takes place in a garden. To lose it was to lose everything. And yet the forest, the primeval garden, also holds a great deal of terror for us. Dante recognized it in The Purgatorio:

> I woke to find myself in a dark wood,
> Where the right road was wholly lost and gone.
> Ay me! how hard to speak of it—that rude
> And rough and stubborn forest! the mere breath
> Of memory stirs the old fear in the blood....

FROM *THE DIVINE COMEDY*,
TRANSLATED BY DOROTHY L. SAYERS

But the desire to go back to that wellspring overcomes our fear. Like Thoreau, in some primitive way we understand that "in wilderness is preservation of the world." Looking for a new landscape, trying to find a place untouched by others, is a kind of longing for renewal, a reaching back into that first garden.

THE CANOE GLIDES with a hushed movement across water surrounded on all sides by the forest. The silence is like velvet. A hawk flashes through the air and plunges toward its prey. As the great, brooding cliffs loom ahead, the only sound is the soft dipping of paddles into glassy water. Totems of a prehistoric age remain etched onto the rock face, symbols and notes of sacred rites left by long-forgotten tribes.

It's difficult to comprehend the profound sense of aloneness a solitary Native traveller must have felt, standing on a monolithic outcrop hundreds of years ago, looking over the vast North American Precambrian forest. A thin wire of smoke spiralling upward from the horizon would have been the only evidence that anyone else might live there. The sound of the forest, the wind moaning through the trees, animals moving stealthily through the underbrush at work and play, roused the need to make a mark on the face of the cliffs.

The ancient wanderer divined spirits living in these rocks surrounded by ferns, lichens, columbines, dwarf birch trees that still manage to find a purchase on what at first appears to be barren stone.

This first garden, this vast silent forest, is filled with myths of a people who knew how to tend it with compassion. The forest held few fears for the First Nations. Here they could worship or find solace. It was a place to come to terms with the forces of spiritual darkness. It was also where they retreated to mend the body. The forest was everything: food, shelter, medicine, religious and physical comfort. It was a cathedral, a storehouse, a hospice.

Even now, walking through an old-growth forest, we find that all the plants that sustained the ancients remain. We are connected with each other and with the past.

FORESTS ARE CONSTANTLY compared to cathedrals, but they are far more mollifying. This is a primitive experience, without the intervening hand of humankind in its making. The forest joins us to the past and to the future as no other place on earth can.

There are no substitutes for trees. They can be a truly transcendent experience. Anyone who has travelled through Cathedral Grove on British Columbia's Vancouver Island or through the small redwood forests of Northern California knows this to be true. Awe is only the first of the emotions these old trees elicit. The light glances off canopies hundreds of feet overhead; the wind softly sighs through the branches in a never-ceasing anthem; the air is almost dizzying, so pure it pains tarnished lungs. There is a connection with a time we have lost almost completely everywhere else. The once-mighty forests that created whole cultures in Europe and Asia have been almost completely wiped out. In North America, logging companies have left small forests as heartbreaking souvenirs of the past. No matter where we go on this earth, our technology—our very touch—has altered reality. We have made changes in nature itself.

PART OF THE HEALING to be derived from landscape comes from developing the ability to listen to what the plants around us have to say—to immerse yourself in looking at a tree, with its vast overhang, to feel the roots plunging deep into the soil. Eventually, there comes a sense of being combined with this solidity, this depth, this long and honourable history.

It's important to listen to trees as well as look at them. During our centuries-long drive to civilize nature, as well as during the process of growing up and leaving childhood behind, we stopped listening to trees and we lost whatever messages they had to tell us. How long has it been since you stood under a tree in spring, leaning up against it to hear the sap flowing? In some trees like the sugar maple, this is almost a roar if you concentrate hard and long enough. Listen to what murmurs through the canopy on a moonlit night. To hold your body against the tree is to feel how the wind moves it sensually from side to side in its youth, or how it stands solidly with age.

WE SHOULD HAVE an empathy with trees more profound than with any other aspect of nature. They have an incredible will to survive, and can adapt to impossible circumstances just as we humans try to do. Yet we continue to cut down trees and mess up the landscape, with little regard for the effect it will ultimately have, not just on the trees but on ourselves. We depend on nature, and yet we have an unfortunate knack for interfering with natural processes and looking at them in isolation, rather than having a sense of nature as an interrelated whole.

Our treatment of trees is just one example. We know that biodiversity is how nature survives—the sheer variety of living things is the glue that holds a region together. This includes the many different species of trees that give birds and animals and insects a home. Biodiversity—and survival—doesn't come from planting thousands of tiny trees of the same species in a tidy row and expecting nature to do the rest. We don't get it right when we try to manufacture a forest. But we can learn how to help nature heal itself, just as we can learn to let nature heal us.

Where I live, there are ominous warnings that, because of an infestation of birch-borers, soon all the birch trees will be dead. A northern landscape that doesn't include the birch would be a poor place. Yet researchers have recently discovered a bacterium that lives in the root system of some species of birch and protects it from borers. So there is hope. If we labour to find out how and why this bacterium works, and if we can unlock still more of nature's complex and closely guarded secrets, we can discover some of the ways nature survives, and help our own race survive in the process.

THE MAGICAL POWERS of plants buried deep in the forest since the beginning of time are only just revealing themselves to the larger world. Modern science has begun to winkle out many of the secrets of these places, whether it be the rain forests or the northern taiga.

Native peoples, in British Columbia or Borneo, have long understood what plants can do. Our technology-oriented society is only now starting to catch up. I like to think that aboriginal peoples lived so completely in harmony with nature that it was easy for them to understand the secrets of the soil, no matter where they lived. It's fascinating that different cultures in different countries have used the same healing plants, or ones that are closely related, in almost the same way and for similar purposes. Discussion continues as to whether this was due to happenstance and good luck or was actually the result of incredible biochemical information that we are still engaged in rediscovering.

We know for certain that the first people in North America, as well as ancient peoples throughout the world, could live off nature and yet not destroy the land, the forest or themselves. They developed what ethnobotanist Mark J. Plotkin, in his extraordinary book *Tales of a Shaman's Apprentice*, calls "botanical ingenuity"; in other words, they eventually figured out the correct dosage that would turn a plant into a medicine rather than a poison. Plotkin cites the example of the mayapple, *Podophyllum peltatum*. Natives of the northeast recognized it was toxic, but they still employed it, in the correct quantities, as a laxative or for curing worms, as well as in an infusion they spread on potato plants to kill bugs.

The secrets of nature used to rest with one or two shamans in the tribe. These early herbalists relied not only on revelations and dreams but on trial and error to build their medicinal repertoire. Much of their information was probably garnered by observing animal behaviour, on the assumption that if it didn't kill them, it probably wouldn't kill humans.

According to legend, a shaman would sit by a plant to discover its spirit and to pray for a revelation of its powers. Out of respect for growing things, an offering of tobacco would be made before anything was harvested (we have rediscovered the fact that tobacco is a pesticide). In some tribes, the shaman would ask permission from one plant to pick plants of the same species growing nearby.

Sometimes a shaman's wisdom was revealed in dreams. If a bear appeared to a sleeper, it was taken to be a vision about plants; bears ate many herbs for their own survival, so they were sure to bring truth to the medicine man. The dream's stories became revealed truth, to be told over and over again; thus the shaman's cumulative wisdom about health, both the body's and the environment's, was passed on.

First Nations people saw—and often still see—the forest quite differently from the way many people look at it now. Each tree had its value. There were no such things as junk trees or weed trees. The poplar, for instance, which we often denigrate as a garbage tree because of its fast-growing nature and its tendency to meander into our sewer systems, was considered a major source of medicine. The bark, leaves and shoots all provided cures for myriad diseases.

What we generally call herbs are those plants used either for food or for medicine—that is, almost anything growing that isn't purely ornamental. What is defined as ornamental, though, has changed with time. In North America, the First Nations used almost every part of the linden tree, *Tilia cordata*, for instance, whereas we know it mainly as a lovely tree that's sometimes used in tea or as a facial refresher.

What indigenous peoples took from nature, they also returned. The remains of fish, for example, would be buried beneath the corn to fertilize it. And every part of a plant, from its roots to its top, was utilized for something. Roots were stored by Native shamans and healers in pieces of bark or bags of twigs and leaves to be made into decoctions (boiled roots or herbs), poultices or compresses.

Some highly aromatic plants, such as those in the ginger family, were known to be rich in essential oils, the basic component of both flavour and medicinal effects. A tea could be made from ginger leaves to help with symptoms of a cold; *Filipendula ulmaria* reduced pain and inflammation (we now call this aspirin); certain poppies, *Papaver somniferum*, relieved pain (codeine); and *Cinchona pubescens* combated malaria (quinine).

The Hopi used bedstraw milkweed, *Asclepias galiodes*, to increase lactation; the Navajo used painted cup, *Castilleja*, for centipede bites. Others used pinroot, *Spigelia marilandica*, to get rid of worms; Seneca snakeroot, *Polygala senega*, for snake bite; and meadowsweet, *Filipendula ulmaria*, for fever, pain and arthritis.

The original idea of herbalism, however, was to treat the whole system—not just the body's immediate symptoms but the spirit as well. Old practitioners never forgot the mind-body connection; the reason for the stomach ache never became secondary to its cure.

PLANTS ARE THE oldest living things on Earth and have a
highly complex structure. Put very simply, photosynthesis
starts the process that turns inorganic molecules into organic
molecules. This, in turn, produces oxygen. Leaves hold much
of a plant's chemical activity and are rich in glycosides,
alkaloids and essential oils, all of which have therapeutic
value. The sap from stems, the sapwood and the outer bark
may also contain medicinal compounds.

If you look at the botanical name of any plant and find
the word *officinalis* or *officinale*, this indicates it has long
been considered an important medicinal plant. Scientists
are beginning to analyze the chemistry of herbs and are
discovering just how complex they are. There are about
265,000 flowering species, but so far we've studied less than
1 per cent for their medicinal value. The other interesting
revelation is that 85 per cent of all drugs are in some way
derived from plants.

We do know that herbs are made up of compounds that work together synergistically. In other words, the combined effect exceeds the sum of the individual components acting separately. Traditional herbal practitioners used the whole plant, rather than just parts of it, and it now seems that, given each herb's chemical intricacies, they were more likely to find effective compounds that way, rather than by isolating the leaves, stems and roots.

The colour in many flowers also has healing properties. For instance, the blooms of German chamomile are rich in essential oils, as are lavender and mint. Even pollen may contain vitamins and minerals. The fruit of such plants as anise, dill, fennel and caraway also contain essential oils. And roots (rhizomes, bulbs and tubers included) store food for the plant and for humans as well. Look at garlic: since the time of the ancient Greeks it has been believed to aid digestion, ward off colds and generally keep the body in good health.

We're in the process of retrieving this ancient wisdom. The World Health Organization estimates that healing herbs are about the only medicine there is for about four billion people, or two-thirds of the world's population. It's obvious that the Western world, with our love of synthetics and technology, is in the minority.

I REMEMBER GOING to a lecture during the 1960s given by the great explorer Thor Heyerdahl. He had just finished one of his monumental journeys on a small balsa-wood sailing craft across the lower part of the Atlantic Ocean, in an attempt to discover how earlier cultures had made the same journey hundreds of years ago. He was filled with rage. Everywhere he found our own civilization all too apparent. People's garbage drifted in the wilds of the ocean. He saw huge, floating islands of oil from distant spills. It was the first time I'd heard the phrase "Man fouling his own nest."

We seem determined not to rely on nature, a curious thing since we are so much a part of it. We do our best to replicate it, to make synthetics of it so we can have a supposedly reliable source for our own needs, without thinking of the consequences.

In the beginning was the garden of Eden. What we will soon have, if we're not careful, is a paradise lost.

A Brief History of the Healing Garden

The very first gardens were, in one sense, healing gardens. Native peoples around the globe learned the properties of the plants growing around them and used them in their healing rites. The most recent archeological finds show that this activity is at least 60,000 years old. And when humans began actively to cultivate gardens, as opposed to availing themselves of nature's bounty, one of the first things they grew, other than food, was herbs.

EVIDENCE OF EARLY gardens shows that they were divided into four sections to symbolize the four elements of water, fire, air and earth, with water forming the quadrants. This design heavily influenced all gardens that came later.

The imagery of the Persian garden was based on the desert oasis. A formal garden, however, unlike an oasis, was always a highly geometric (usually rectangular), enclosed space, designed with a high regard for the landscape around it. This was a place for contemplation. Water was included, of course, because it was such a precious commodity, and where there was water, there would certainly be an oasis or a garden.

As Muslims established outreaches in Spain, North Africa, Turkey, Central Asia and Mogul India, so the influence of their gardens spread. The sense of coolness and privacy, with a focus on water, has become the heart of the healing garden.

THE TRADITION OF herbal healing has carried on for thousands upon thousands of years. The Chinese began recording their use of herbs around 3400 BC. Legend has it that the mythic Emperor Shen Nung, the god who invented agriculture, tested herbs on himself. Unfortunately, he died, it seems, of an overdose—all herbs can be toxic if they are used in excess, even by such a god-like creature. Before he died, though, the Emperor composed the *Pen-ts'ao Ching,* or *The Classic Herbal,* around 2700 BC. (It's thought that the text was transcribed in the first century and had 252 prescriptions listed. The dynasties that followed elaborated on it, until the definitive form of the *Pen-ts'ao Ching* was produced between AD 25 and 220.)

By 500 BC, Egyptian herbalists were practising all around the Mediterranean, spreading their knowledge and their plants. The Greeks of Aristotle's time (384–322 BC) established the four humours: blood, phlegm, yellow bile and black bile, to parallel the earth, air, fire and water of what was then considered the definitive world order. Ancient Greeks believed the body should be rid of its excesses, and thus relied heavily on sweating, diuretics, enemas and laxatives, as well as using parsley, thyme and fennel to improve the flow of urine.

For their part, the Romans were enthusiastic about blood-letting, although, like the Greeks, they also saw the merits of a balanced diet and plenty of exercise. Medicinally, both cultures used theriacs—a combination of many herbs—but as a general cure-all, they leaned heavily toward opiates and antispasmodics. The Romans were known to have used senna and castor oil as laxatives, but they also cared for the spirit as well as the body, perfuming their villas with lavender and other fragrant herbs to create an uplifting mood. And both Greeks and Romans used herbs, which were seen as elements of purification and healing, in their sacred rites.

In the first century, Pliny the Elder, a Roman, wrote *Naturalis Historia*, a series of 37 books, one of which concentrates on kitchen gardens and another on both cultivated and wild flowers. Dioscorides, a first-century Greek physician, wrote *De Materia Medica*, which became one of the earliest and most influential manuscripts on medicinal plants.

SPICES WERE AT the root of Arab culture, and spice routes developed all through North Africa, southern Europe and southern Asia. Even Mohammed himself (570–632) was a spice merchant for a while. Given their peripatetic lives, Muslims gathered a comprehensive knowledge of spices and herbs that was very much a part of their culinary, artistic and healing traditions. Arabic medical schools incorporated Greek studies with their own discoveries, and Avicenna (980–1037), a Persian, wrote *The Canon of Medicine* based on Greek texts by Hippocrates, Aristotle, Dioscorides and Galen, plus his own pharmacology.

Arab countries designed gardens using roses, jasmine, lilies, pomegranates and almond with hedges of myrtle, a tradition that was carried on into the medieval Christian period. The great era of Muslim empire-building ended in the thirteenth century with the invasion of the Mongols.

THE FIRST CHRISTIAN monastery was founded in AD 305 in northern Egypt, and a small enclosed garden was included. By the time the Benedictine order was established near Rome in AD 540, gardening was very much part of monastery life. By the ninth century, monks all over Europe, transcribing from much earlier Greek and Latin texts, were formulating the first herbals. Both Pliny's *Naturalis Historia* and Dioscorides' *De Materia Medica* were translated and laboriously copied by medieval monks, who also copied later manuscripts. A version of *De Materia*, called *Codex Vindobonensis*, was made around 512 (it has been housed in the National Library in Vienna since the late sixteenth century).

Until this point, knowledge of herbal healing had been the preserve either of educated men with access to the manuscripts or of women, who had a small repertoire of healing herbs that they passed on to their daughters.

Much valuable information, particularly from these women, was lost during the so-called Dark Ages—perhaps because of the plagues that raged across Europe. These pestilences, not surprisingly, were terrifying, particularly since no one seemed able to come up with a cure. And when people are frightened, they often become irrational. When they realized that the healing women in their communities had no answers for the awful diseases that were rampaging through whole countries, they persecuted them. Rather than celebrating these women, who used their knowledge as best they could to heal as much as they could, thousands were burned at the stake as witches, vilified as heathens or driven to practise secretly if they wished to continue using what were known as "simples"—easily found and gathered herbs that could be employed in everyday healing.

The healing arts went underground in Europe, and as a result, gardening records either were never made in the first place or were destroyed. There are passing references to plants in other, unrelated documents, and gardens are depicted in some paintings, but virtually all specific records of European medieval gardening have disappeared.

IN THE CAROLINGIAN period (Charlemagne's reign, 800–814), gardens for food and medicine were being built all over the empire, which covered most of Europe. The evidence we have left are gardens in Germany and Switzerland where we can see the design basic to the later physic gardens (gardens created for physicians): a quadrant (taken from earlier Islamic gardens) with herbs, some ornamental flowers and some vegetables for the table, the whole laid out in a central cross. The lily, the rose, flag iris and sage were particularly important to these gardens, not only for their strong symbolic references to purity but for their scent and beauty as well.

By the eleventh century, Greek medicine was going through a revival, the principal texts having been translated from Arabic to French and then into Latin. Perhaps because of the monks' work in copying manuscripts, and certainly because a knowledge of Greek and Latin was essential in order to read these texts, the practice of medicine was very much under the thumb of the church, which was, of course, dominated by men. However, one of the great thinkers of the period was a woman, Hildegard of Bingen (1098–1179). She wrote *Physica*, a herbal that blended folk medicine, mysticism, vision and practical experience.

THE KNOWLEDGE OF herbs that medieval priests and monks were beginning to accumulate was supplemented by the plants and information that knights brought back during the Crusades of the eleventh and twelfth centuries. Despite the turbulent times, pilgrims also continued to march, merchants to trade and scholars to wander throughout Europe and the Middle East, bringing knowledge and plants home with them. In Salerno, Italy, a medical school was established in the ninth century by Adale the Arab, Salernus the Latin, Pontus the Greek and Elinus the Jew, combining the wisdom of all schools of thought. It continued to flourish until the fifteenth century.

THE MEDIEVAL EUROPEAN gardens are the most interesting of all, perhaps because we know so little about them. Our scanty knowledge is based on sources peripheral to horticulture; substantial archives on gardens begin only in the thirteenth century. Though the medieval enclosed gardens were never built within the cloisters of abbeys, they were installed nearby, making them convenient both as a pharmacy and as a kitchen garden, which was incorporated with the herbs.

In Milan, there was apparently a Cistercian monastery that gives some idea of the importance of these gardens. Each monk's cell had its own small herb garden attached. It was the monk's one contact with the world—essential not only to his spiritual life but to his physical well-being. Since the order observed a vow of silence, this was his sole means of communication. It doesn't take much of a stretch to know what love and energy must have gone into these little patches of ground.

BY THE RENAISSANCE, a change in attitudes toward gardening was starting to take place. Botanists were travelling around the world and bringing back exotic species. Thousands of plants new to the old world were being introduced, and a great deal of work was being invested in "improving" existing species. The dawn of the modern idea of nature had begun: Humans were superior to nature and could manipulate it as they wished.

The content of a garden was changing too. For a long time, medicinal plants had been emphasized, but now, people began to place more and more plants in their gardens purely for pleasure. Plants became collectibles, and gardens (for the rich, that is) became much more elaborate.

Knot gardens—formal areas planted in patterns outlined by carefully cropped hedges of rosemary and lavender—became a fashion by about the fifteenth century. By planting herbs along with fruit and ornamental flowers, it was possible to keep each fragrance, and every foliage texture was set apart and emphasized. It was a perfect way to jam in masses and masses of plants but still retain an overall sense of organization and control, creating a serene tapestry of plants to please the eye as well as the nostrils.

There were, too, pleasing contrasts for the visitor, places to rest, to view, to breathe in the air. To heal. And healing was as much a part of these gardens as was the beauty of the designs and the usefulness of the plants. The sixteenth-century physic gardens were the beneficiaries of the exotic plants that explorers were bringing back to Europe, and gardeners' knowledge expanded exponentially.

Along with renewed interest came the desire for more information. The first print edition of Dioscorides' *De Materia Medica* was made by Pietro Mattioli in Venice in 1544; it influenced all later herbals and was used—in adaptations and translations, in manuscript and printed form—right up to the eighteenth century.

In 1590, Li Shi Zhen published the 54-volume *Compendium of Materia Medica.* It contained descriptions of 2,000 drugs derived mainly from plants. Again, in terms of so-called modern progress, it's interesting to see that *Ephedra sinica,* mahuang, was clearly mentioned in these texts as a herb that improved circulation and suppressed coughs, but it was not rediscovered until this century.

Chapter Two

One of the greatest and most influential herbals of all was published in England in 1597 by John Gerard. Titled *Gerard's Herball*, it came complete with 1,800 woodcuts. Nearly as famous is *The English Physician* by Nicholas Culpeper, published in 1652 and controversial from the start because of the author's insistence in lacing the book with astrology. Both *Gerard's Herball* and *The English Physician* were published in English, not Latin, and as a result they were extremely popular with a large number of people. Their accessible language also meant that they were among the herbals that broke down medicine's exclusivity, since before their publication, an extensive knowledge of the discipline was restricted to scholars who could read the earlier texts in Greek or Latin.

THE DOCTRINE OF SIGNATURES—the belief that like cures like—became popular in seventeenth-century Europe. The shape, or even the colour, of a leaf or root was supposed to indicate the healing properties that a plant possessed. Since walnuts look like the brain, for example, they were thought to have been good for the mind, while the liverwort or liverleaf, *Hepatica americana*, being shaped like the liver, was held to be a liver tonic.

During the eighteenth century, the Age of Reason, Europeans became more introspective, and began to study nature less and their own natures more. Even though luminaries such as the English scientist Joseph Priestley proved, in the early nineteenth century, that plants can flourish in foul air and restore oxygen to a degenerated environment, people were afraid to have plants indoors, believing they would poison the atmosphere. It wasn't until later in the nineteenth century that plants were once again regarded as life-sustaining, not life-inhibiting.

Meanwhile, people had created false categories, dividing plants into those they ate, those they needed for medicine or something they harvested for its usefulness. For a long time, we didn't see plants as part of a whole, or ourselves as fitting into that whole.

The history of herbalism has since led to a division between those who practice it in some form and those who scorn anything that isn't sanctioned by the medical establishment. During the eighteenth and nineteenth centuries, indiscriminate blood-letting probably killed more people than herbs ever did. But herbalism went underground, only resurfacing in the early nineteenth century when German chemist/physician Samuel Hahnemann experimented with botanical drugs (quinine being one of them) until he developed his theories of homeopathy, which basically holds that small doses of natural medicines will result in the body triggering its own protective mechanisms.

Finally, in the latter part of this century, the study of botanical medicines took on a new sheen as we discovered the old ways were not all crazed, ineffective or downright bad for you. Digitalis is one well-known drug that came from folk medicine, as did reserpine, a tranquillizer derived from *Rauvolfia serpentina*, Indian snakeroot, that was much used in the 1950s.

THE MORE I READ about the history of gardens, the more I find researching the way we garden a fascinating form of social history. Our changing attitudes to nature reflect each century's cultural shifts. I feel a particular connection with early gardens, particularly those of medieval times, since my own garden seems to echo some of the plant arrangements I've seen in drawings and paintings of the period. The squares of plants and stones in my garden hold many different kinds of flowers, herbs and shrubs, giving a feel of a tapestry. My garden doesn't look like a painting, but I like to think I'm carrying on an ancient tradition.

RIGHT: *Garden writer Elisabeth Sheldon has created brilliant colour and warmth in one corner of her garden.* (PHOTOGRAPH BY MARJORIE HARRIS)

OVERLEAF: *A calming and restful combination of lamb's ears,* Stachys byzantina; *and* Rosa complicta. (PHOTOGRAPH BY PADDY WALES IN THE GARDEN OF JILL TAYLOR)

3

Contemporary Horticultural Therapy

A garden cannot mend a broken bone, but a garden can repair a damaged soul, recover a person's lost spirit, recall events from the distant past and restore an exhausted body. Hospital patients sleep more easily in a room filled with lavender potpourri. Lavender will also heal a cut or create a bouquet. If a garden can heal itself, it can heal us. Pulling out a few weeds, learning the name of a new plant, digging something up and moving it are all pursuits we instinctively know are good for us—and good for the plants, too.

*D*espite the dozens of new ways to look
at the world—the genetic, the microscopic,
the chemical—we are still very much the
same people who built Stonehenge so that
each year we could make sure the sun really
did begin its retreat, the same people who
trembled at eclipses.

THE DEATH OF NATURE,
WILLIAM MCKIBBEN

THE RESTORATIVE QUALITY of nature has been built into almost every cultural heritage, starting in ancient times when walled gardens were created by the Persians to keep out the forces of chaos and make an oasis of refreshment, and on to the little downtown, city courtyard that's a respite from the polluted and noisy world beyond.

We need nature near us in some form or another, partly because our attachment to nature is primordial. We evolved along with plants, and we are, in many senses, one with them. This is called biophilia, which is defined by scientists as an innate affinity and reverence for living things, and the sense of satisfaction to be derived from gazing on a natural scene.

Even though we seem to have lost our way by demonstrating far too often just how dismally we can treat nature, we've made some progress in how we treat the sick among us. Patients in hospitals or people who are physically confined in some way are now being helped by using some aspect of gardening to restore their quality of life.

This approach to ameliorating a sick person's condition through the healing powers of nature has, of course, been with us for a long time, but it has gained momentum over the last century or so. In 1865, American landscape architect Frederick Law Olmsted (the designer of Central Park in New York), wrote in a paper entitled "The Value and Care of Parks" that nature "employs the mind without fatigue and yet exercises it; tranquillizes it and yet enlivens it; and thus, through the influence of the mind over the body, gives the effect of refreshing rest and reinvigoration to the whole system." Olmsted firmly believed that any aspect of nature introduced to cities brings "tranquillity and rest to the mind."

The term "horticultural therapy" was coined back in the early 1900s by Dr. Karl and Dr. Will Menninger at their foundation, the well-known Menninger Clinic in Kansas. Gardening, they discovered, opened the eyes of their psychiatric patients to the wider world, provided a reason for them to socialize, gave them enjoyment, developed their motor skills and implanted in them a huge measure of self-esteem.

A number of studies have been conducted since the 1970s to try to understand this link between people and nature. Horticultural therapy is increasingly becoming accepted as a sound method of aiding drug addicts, schizophrenics, Alzheimer patients, disabled children and other people in trouble.

Roger S. Ulrich, a landscape architect at the Texas A & M University, who has done some of the most important work in this area in the past decade, talks about people's intense reactions to plants. He found that greenery elicits both emotional and physiological responses that play critical roles in the restoration of the body. Those same feelings become central, he says, to subsequent thoughts and memories, and ultimately to a person's behaviour with respect to his or her environment.

Another researcher, Charles Lewis, of Morton Arboretum in Illinois, discovered what an intimate and intense message people seem to receive from plants. The most immediate is one of steadiness. "The gardener sees that change need not be disruptive," Lewis wrote, "but can be part of a dynamic stability. How different this is from our technological society, where the flow of life is constricted by schedule and regulation, and must change rapidly to accommodate fads and other distractions where people are under threat by new, man-made terrors."

These and other studies have found that once patients begin to work with plants, no matter how old or how fierce the disability, they gain self-esteem, confidence and a feeling of usefulness. They bring back to their lives a quality that makes us truly human: the ability to nurture.

We don't need studies to know that our profound connection with plants has to do with nurturing. We look after plants much as we do our children. Think of how often you talk to your plants, call them "little guys" and treat them gently and tenderly.

If someone is depressed or withdrawn, having a plant or two to care for can give them a sense of future. Subconsciously, the patient probably feels: I must get better so I can see the plants bloom. This is especially true in overcoming a sense of loss. Handling plants brings a person back into touch with the changing cycles of life and death. It also adds another dimension to time—patience—in waiting for a blossom to open up or a shoot to appear from a seed.

In one study conducted in a prison, the inmates who had cells that looked out at a small copse of trees checked into the infirmary far fewer times than those with only a brick wall to stare at. In another study that involved two cases where the conditions for a gall bladder operation were identical, the patient who had a view of trees and shrubs recovered more quickly after the operation, needed fewer pain-killing drugs and was released from the hospital earlier than the one with no view.

There is no doubt that patients get better faster if they can see something growing. The garden really does heal. By actually working with plants, people are drawn out of themselves. Institutions with garden programs for patients find that the sick respond quickly, violence abates in the mentally ill and everyone becomes more responsive to the world around them.

WE'VE IGNORED THE healing powers of plants and gardens for far too long in our rush toward technological solutions to disease. A garden may not cure an incurable disease, but think how much anxiety is relieved with a little distraction, how a sensual moment can make life a little bit better. If the plant lives, so can I.

ANYONE WHO HAS EVER worked in a windowless office knows that the first thing you do is put up a poster of a glorious landscape. Even this seemingly superficial contact with nature is important. One study conducted in a dental clinic found that on days when posters depicting such a scene were present, the patients' fears were allayed much more easily than when there was nothing on the wall. It didn't matter if the patients actually noticed or commented on the pictures. Even if plants or scenes of plants are taken in unconsciously, they still give a measure of comfort.

NASA interviewed their astronauts extensively on what they needed most during their flights to outer space. Their response was: almost anything that would connect them with the natural world—from the colours used inside the spacecraft (nothing neon) to plants to posters depicting natural scenes (mountain waterfalls or savanna-like scenes were the favourites). Cultural background made no difference: both American and Russian astronauts felt the same way.

All the studies done on alpha-wave activity in the brain—which leads to a wakeful but relaxed state—indicate that it is higher when people look at a natural setting with lots of vegetation. Blood pressure lowers, muscle tension relaxes, the skin warms. And recovery time from stressful situations (everything from an operation to exams to a difficult work situation) was speeded up when people looked at slides of a landscape—not even the real thing.

This has astounding implications in terms of our need for nature. It's clear that we must feel nature is somewhere close by—even if we don't actually notice it all the time—or we are bereft.

Nature holds our attention and diverts it away from ourselves, from our worries. It engages us in loftier thoughts, giving a sense of creativity while providing comfort at the same time. Nature nurtures. Nature aids in meditation.

ANOTHER BOND BETWEEN ourselves and the natural world is the miraculous way in which plants protect themselves. When a tree is assaulted, by man or beast, all its forces rush to defend the area under attack by closing that section to preserve the rest of the tree. When a plant is attacked by bugs, the plant knows how to save itself. We have discovered that plants have an immune system similar to ours, which helps safeguard them from future attacks. Eventually they build up an immunity that can be passed on to future generations of plants as part of their genetic makeup.

HORTICULTURAL THERAPIST Mitchell Hewson, who directs the program at the Homewood Health Centre in Guelph, Ontario, gives talks about the many kinds of approach to this new form of caring. First and perhaps most important, it must be meaningful to the patient, not just busy time. Hewson had one patient, a model, who, after a mastectomy, fell into a deep, almost suicidal depression. She participated in his program in a desultory way, but when she started a class about how to design with flowers, she was taken right out of herself and her woes. She became such an accomplished florist that she is now a professional. "Though she felt she'd lost some of her own beauty," Hewson says, "she's able to create beauty that is an extension of herself."

ONE OF THE VINES that draws me inexorably into the garden is *C. tenuifolia*, sweet autumn clematis. The tiny white flowers clamber over every bit of visible territory, whether it happens to be covered with other vines or not. The scent of vanilla fills the air, and bees adore this vine. Apart from its aesthetic qualities, the sweet smell of vanilla, as research indicates, will calm the nerves of people going in for chemotherapy.

This is a part of what's called aromatherapy, an epithet with a thudding New Age ring that's enough to throw some people off. But wait. It is folly to ignore just how much smell can affect our lives and our feelings.

The term aromatherapy was coined in the 1930s by René-Maurice Gattefosse, but it dates back hundreds of years before that. The basic technique was first used in the Middle East and brought back to Europe by the Crusaders.

The idea is to extract the scent from a specific blossom by maceration—reducing the flowers to a soft mass by soaking them in liquid—and then distilling them into essential oils. It may take kilos and kilos of blooms to create the resulting light oils—the highly volatile and easily vaporized essence of the blooms—which can be absorbed by the skin.

Essential oils are the linchpins of aromatherapy. Adherents believe that the oils of certain plants can heal us directly. They can be absorbed through the skin or inhaled, used in massage or a bath, or smoothed over the body in the form of creams and lotions.

A NEW AREA of research has recently opened up called Aroma-Chology: the study of the interrelationships between psychology and fragrance technology. Scientists want to find out more about the effect of aroma on behaviour. Do we feel more festive if the house is filled with pine scent at Christmas? Will spring happen, in our hearts at least, if a hyacinth is forced into bloom? The human spirit is one of hope. And scent often cheers us on. But can we be manipulated by scent? Scientists seem to think so. One of their contentions is that lavender increases alpha waves, which relax the body, and jasmine increases beta waves, which make us more alert.

Surveys of how people feel about scent are revealing:

- Scent improves the overall quality of life.
- Many different odours will help keep people more alert (lemon and lavender are two of the most important).
- Scent is a powerful retriever of lost memories.

THE GARDEN'S HEALING WAYS are different for each person. My friend Jan is confined to a wheelchair because of crippling rheumatoid arthritis. She writes: "Forgive me if I do not use the word 'spiritual' because I don't know what spirit is. Does my garden heal? Physically, I think not. Mentally, I think it may well calm a troubled mind. It does, however, give life meaning and makes illness easier to bear."

Though she knows her physical condition will lead to early death, Jan can say, without a touch of self-pity, "The garden has a somewhat 'till death do us join' component to it."

As she sits outside with the late-day sun touching her proud face, musing over the year, she writes, "I feel a complete empathy just sitting on the deck, whether I'm listening to the sough of the trees or the chanting of tree frogs, watching the birds feasting on pine-cone seeds or the groundhog protecting her five little ones as she faces off the cat; or observing the onset of spring as it slowly gains momentum and the bulbs thrust up through the grass, the wrens nest and depart, the chipmunks, their cheeks bulging, strut the paths again and the leafy trees block my view of the chicken barn and Mount Nemo—once more shrouding me in a dense, green, secret garden, where the sheer uninhibited power of Nature continues unabated, regardless of me and my other world, for yet another year.

"I am part of this garden," she continues. "My ancestry is woven into the fabric of this half-billion-year-old wonder called Nature, in an intricate manner I will never fathom. My garden is a learning, loving, teaching, sensual, artistic experience, giving me a reason to live and a reason to die. My children know to strew my ashes on the earth and not weep for me. They know there will be another whisper in the trees when my winter comes."

RIGHT: Rosa complicta *is one of the loveliest of roses. Here it seems to reflect simplicity to perfection.* (PHOTOGRAPH BY PADDY WALES IN THE GARDEN OF AUDREY LITHERLAND)

OVERLEAF: *A field of lavender and poppies is one of those bits of serendipity that creates the healing process.* (PHOTOGRAPH BY MARJORIE HARRIS IN THE GARDEN OF LYNDA DOWLING, HAPPY VALLEY HERB FARM)

Wildlife in the Garden

There is a wonderful Chinese proverb that says: "A bird does not sing because it has an answer—it sings because it has a song." This seems transparent when I listen to the joy that fills the air. The other day I was walking about quietly in my garden, or maybe I was just standing still, breathing in the ripeness all around, when a bird flew from the middle of one fence to the other. It was so near, I could feel the air stir around me from the beat of its wings.

THE HEALING GARDEN includes wildlife, plus a few domestic forms for good measure. These creatures remind us that, although we may have lost our way in Paradise, *they* never left it. Somehow the presence of animals connects us once again with a more innocent time. And this connection makes the importance of wildlife paramount to the healing garden.

Since I never spray or use noxious chemicals in my garden, I've got lots of buzzing, sucking and general merriment all the time, in all seasons. Sometimes it stuns me just how much noise and activity are going on out there.

At times during the autumn, when the fruit on the old pear tree up the street is particularly ripe, dozens of birds of all stripes and species come every day to have their fill, larking about and making a general hubbub. The crows spend a huge amount of time complaining about what the pigeons are doing, and all the other birds move about picking up berries here, seeds there. There are evergreens they can nest in, there are shrubs that bloom in different seasons, which have berries with a variety of sugars and fats for each special need.

Winterberry, *Ilex verticillata*, is a good choice because it has such bright red berries. And the elder is sheer bliss. It arches over into my neighbour's garden and the birds head for it first. The magnificent ebony-black clusters provide a rare feast. The *Rosa glauca*, with its fat, orange hips, has a pair of cardinals and at least half a dozen house finches that make it their own for most of the long winter months. And everywhere around the garden there are native grasses laden down with seeds. Bluestem, *Andropogon virginicus*, switchgrass, *Panicum virgatum*, and Northern sea oats, *Chasmanthium latifolium*, are among my favourites and, serendipitously, they attract birds like crazy.

I've planted these for myself, but they also serve as a stop-gap during migration for hundreds of birds. I love to watch the garden when it's flooded in spring and see at least a dozen of them flapping about in the water with sheer pleasure.

What's good for wildlife turns out to be very easy on the eyes as well. Porcelain ampelopsis, *Ampelopsis brevipedunculata* 'Variegata,' has a turquoise-blue berry that look like faux jewellery. Leaves of the Virginia creeper, *Parthenocissus quinquefolia*, turn a spectacular colour in the autumn, like banners enticing the migrating birds to come and eat the fruit, which is high in the fat needed for their long journey ahead. And the bittersweet, *Celastrus scandens*, has gem-like orange berries that attract sapsuckers and flickers. How gorgeously nature clads itself, and how usefully.

What may look like visual chaos in early winter actually means that the garden is filled with forage for animals and birds. Before the frost has totally destroyed them, the four-o'clocks, *Mirabilis jalapa*, make so many seeds, it's impossible to know what will turn up next year. This profligacy may produce red, yellow, pink or white flowers, or a mix of all of them. And they attract hummingbirds all summer long.

THEN THERE ARE the bees. I became fascinated with them,
partly because there is a huge hive in between the roof and
walls of a house down the street. Every time the exterminators
come, the gardeners gather around saying, "No poisons,"
which gets rid of the exterminators. So the bees live on, not
bothering anyone that I've heard of, busy with all there is to
do in the neighbourhood.

The exciting thing about having a city garden is that
it is a way station not only for migrating birds, but for
butterflies as well. I didn't make the connection between
the movement of butterflies and the importance of my little
garden until I saw six monarchs sipping from the giant bloom
of Joe-Pye weed, *Eupatorium purpureum.* They attended my
garden because I grow this plant that is so special to them.
I watched them tremble on the blossoms for the better part
of an hour.

Once they'd stopped dipping for nectar, they rested in the
warmth of the sun. I was so close I could almost see the tiny
scales that make up the colour on their wings. From a
distance, they all looked more or less the same, but from this
proximity they were individuals.

Looking closely at nature is important in healing. In pain or in sickness, we feel as if we are alone. When we observe nature at work, we are aware almost immediately of the extraordinary sense of peace that takes over the mind and probably the soul. The sense that we are not alone, the sense of being attached to that former innocence, makes a pause in what can be, during an illness, relentless terror.

Imagine being part of a flock of butterflies on the long migratory route from Mexico, attempting to find milkweeds in the vast urban sprawl. They must feel desperate, I should think. We have even more empathy with the magnificent monarchs since they were struck down in their own secret forests, not just because of an unseasonable snow in Mexico but because the forest had been logged in such a way that there was very little shelter for them. The sight of a million dead monarch butterflies due to human carelessness and natural causes is enough to chill anyone's heart.

It's even more important, then, to put as much stuff in your garden as possible for every type of butterfly. Painted ladies on thistles, monarchs on milkweeds, others on nettles. They also love herbs such as thyme, bronze fennel and mint.

Gardeners should have a sense of stewardship toward these animals. As far as healing goes, that stewardship contributes immeasurably to our feelings of usefulness in the scheme of things at a time when, if we are ill, we often feel quite useless.

Individualizing animals also brings them closer to us. I never noticed the dark eye spots some butterflies have on their wings, put there so that a predatory bird will think it's facing an owl. A butterfly's wings are covered with scales of pure light, arranged so patterns emerge that will attract the same species. You can only see this if you take time to observe.

Butterflies are extraordinary. They have a genetic ability to follow the earth's magnetic fields in getting around. They have a limited sense of smell, but are attracted to brightly coloured flowers (especially pure reds and oranges). They like erect blooms with a rim to land on, preferably with dots or lines to guide them to the centre of the blossom. Think about all of that each time you buy a plant. It definitely slows you down and takes you out of yourself.

The healing garden is not so much one of elaborate showiness, good design or a display of taste but something more profound. It is a means of connecting with other living creatures in the community we share. It is a way of discovering both empathy and sympathy for their survival. You become so intimate with the garden's life that the symbiosis between garden and gardener becomes complete. And the healing garden performs its miracles.

THERE IS NO LESS activity at night in the garden than there is during the day. I often feel the need to wait outside for darkness. I sit and watch the light fade. The reds go first; then the purple loses its red and turns to blue; the greys of artemisias stand out like clouds; then the yellows and whites begin to gleam in the moonlight. Bird songs sound louder in the evening air; in fact, I've been in places where the noise is almost deafening.

My goal is to catch a glimpse of a luna moth. This elusive creature is rare in my area. Like all moths, it has wings covered with scales, but unlike many other moths, we know very little about the luna and its life cycle remains enigmatic. While butterflies have great eyesight and a lousy sense of smell, moths depend on night aromas, which are as distinctive as those of the daytime.

Moths have developed long tongues to cope with the tube-like flowers that attract them. In my own garden, they flutter around the evening primroses and heliotropes I keep in pots. One of the night sounds we used to hear were the frogs. Sadly, they've been almost eliminated from my city—yet another reminder of how drastically we've altered the natural world. But I have hope that the toads that live in the neighbourhood will survive here. Each night their tuneful company is joined by silent bats that sweep through the garden air.

The garden at night stands for mystery, something we should all have in our lives. We need to draw the moonlight in with a little water. At the full moon, I enjoy watching it, both in the sky above and reflected below in a bowl of water left out for the bugs. I've hung mirrors outside to bounce the pale moonlight off the deck and illuminate everything around me, and at those moments, I feel as though I am bathed in magic. This peacefulness stays with me all night long.

The Sensual Garden

The faint footprints of nightly visits from wild animals and the cats who use this place as part of their territorial wanderings are everywhere. The raucous raccoons have been scratching up paths looking for succulent grubs. The mysterious, evasive skunk has left a strong pattern of scent. This is my first contact with the garden at sunrise, as plants spray oxygen into the morning air.

THIS CONTACT AWAKENS ME to the core of my soul. The yeasty quality here determines how I will go about my day. I poke about, using everything but my brain. What I touch, smell and see at first light makes me leave the need to ratiocinate behind. I am more alive in this moment, more aware and more closely tied to all my senses.

Scent

> And because the breath of flowers is far
>
> sweeter in the air, where it comes and goes,
>
> like the warbling of music, than in the hand,
>
> therefore nothing is more fit for that delight
>
> than to know what the flowers and plants
>
> that do best perfume the air.

Of Gardens,
Francis Bacon

THIS IS PERHAPS the most compelling of all the senses. We use it with every breath we take without thinking about it. But imagine a life without smell. A blank canvas, a beginning, surely, but not completely alive. Its potency is especially apparent when we sniff the air and remember things from the past.

Recently I walked into a garden with a pot of zinnias sitting on a table. I don't grow them—it's something about the severity of that orange. Yet I felt strangely impelled to bury my head in the blooms, and was instantly transported back to my grandmother's garden. I could *see* a whole drift of them planted in one corner. This was a place that had not come to my mind in almost 50 years—I was last there when I was six—but I could clearly visualize the mass of zinnias and marigolds beside the chicken coop that upset the whole of her downtown neighbourhood.

I told a friend about my visceral experience with the smell of the zinnias. She said, "For me, it's peas. I won't even let my children get to them before I do. I must be there first. The minute I smell them, I must eat them straight off the vine. Suddenly, I'm home again in England."

Smell is the first thing that hits me when I walk into the garden. Taking a deep breath can abate all the emotions that build up toxins in my body. No more than a few feet into the garden and I am transported.

I understand completely how aromatherapy came into existence. On a clear September morning, I can count the scents that hang in the air, and feel the better for it. Taking out last night's dinner parings to the compost is the first chore of each day. There is the smell of the food, which is slightly acidic, with the fruit and vegetables beginning to turn, but not unpleasant. There is the camphor-like smell of asters, the sweetness of buddleias about to draw butterflies to warm in the early morning sun. *Helichrysum angustifolium*, or curry plant, lives up to its name as I brush by the pot. It seems even more vigorous in the September air.

Diverted by the wealth of bouquets in the garden, I forget whatever it is I was supposed to be worried about and start to pick up things, take a swipe at an unruly plant. I am off into another, better world.

Why do we get so carried away by all this pungency? In *A Natural History of the Senses*, Diane Ackerman points out that not only can we detect over 10,000 different odours, but smell sends messages straight into our limbic system—a mysterious, archaic and intensely emotional section of the brain in which we feel, lust and invent.

The aroma of herbs has been used for centuries to improve living conditions. Lavender and thyme were strewn over the mud floors of medieval homes to keep diseases such as typhus at bay, and probably discouraged mice, lice and a few other insects as well.

Over the past few years, enough research has been done on how fragrance affects us to come up with some surprising facts. A lemony scent will apparently urge factory workers to produce more efficiently. Peppermint can speed up the typist. Any flower odour will aid concentration. On finding this out, I immediately freshen all the potpourri in my office with lavender. The atmosphere is much improved.

It becomes clear why the smell of flowers has such an effect on humans when you realize that scent indicates the plant's sex life has gone into overdrive and it is ripe to draw in whatever insect it needs for fertilization. This burst of fecundity is announced by sending out an intoxicating scent. And because of the co-operative nature of nature, there will always be an insect ready to do the flower's bidding, so both of them can survive.

I COULD NOT BEAR to go into the garden without bending over to fondle a sage plant. Warmed slightly by the sun, the rough, grey leaves, once squeezed, release oils onto my fingertips. All at once Thanksgiving dinner comes rushing into my mind. I can smell the family coming close to the table to have one of the best celebrations of the year. How perfect to celebrate how fortunate we are in the middle of the richness of autumn. It is the best time of the year.

Even if I had only a balcony, I would grow sage, not just because I love the taste of it in my cooking, but because it encompasses memories and brings back those wonderful (and sometimes awful) times. Thanksgiving, Easter, Christmas— sage holds each occasion locked in its spicy scent, waiting to be liberated.

[It is] to thread our days with subtle, gentle happiness,
a happiness definable but profoundly felt. To sleep
in a room beyond whose casement Honeysuckle
scrambles and to awake in the night to the exquisite
fragrance that inspires the darkness is an experience
of rare quality. Such things invade life's commonplace
routine with an ecstatic pleasure.

THE FRAGRANT GARDEN,
LOUISE BEEBE WILDER

ONCE EVENING DRAWS to a close, certain blooms, curled up
all day long, slowly open, to allow their aroma to drift about,
beckoning the evening moths to sip. Other blossoms have a
musty smell that subtly draws bats to drink.

Stocks, nicotiana, tropical orchids, gladiolus, heliotropes,
phloxes and madonna lilies are all plants that emit their scent
in the evening. They make a perfect arrangement on their
own, in glistening white or rich deep purple. Even shrubs
such as *Daphne cineorum* are pollinated by moths
when they bloom in spring. And the Russian olive, *Elaeagnus
angustifolia,* has a sweetness to its rather insignificant flower
that needs close proximity to appreciate.

There are annuals that make the night-scented garden strange and exotic enough to excite every nerve end. Angel's trumpet, *Datura inoxia*, has wonderful long, grey leaves sporting huge, dangling, white trumpets. In tropical countries, they are the size of large shrubs, but here we can only grow them as annuals or in pots. Every single part of the plant is poisonous. Then there's moonflower, *Ipomoea alba*, which looks drab and weary all day long. As the day begins to wane, though, the large, morning-glory-like blossoms unfold in their own form of slow-motion photography. The scent alone is enough to pull you out of doors. Planted around doors and windows, moonflowers also fill the house with a thrilling scent. Other vines, such as honeysuckle, convey the same kind of sensual pleasure.

American writer Louise Beebe Wilder, who was so eloquent about the fragrant garden, talked about how daytime aromas can be quite different from those emitted by night. The true vesper flowers are curious in that few of them have daytime attractions. Bouncing Bet, *Saponaria officinalis,* is one that I grow; evening-scented stock, *Matthiola bicornis,* is another, because they can be combined with bulbs and take over when the bulbs start looking ratty. They also attract moths, which is a bonus.

As the moon rises, *Lavater trimestris*, 'Mont Blanc,' glows in the light; the evening-scented stock, which was a bore during the day, begins its performance. The slightly comic heads of gooseneck loosestrife, *Lysimachia clethroides*, dance about in a friendly drift, breaking up the lowering, increasing darkness.

The halo around the moon drops lightly into the garden to rest in the form of pale moths fluttering over the evening flowers that are opening up and spilling their scent into the air. The hawk moth flutters around plants, drawn by their sweetness. And we, who are arrogant enough to think this display is all for us, are firmly put in our places—just a part of the sublime scene.

Sight

Into your garden you can walk

And with each plant and flower talk;

View all their glories, from each one

Raise some rare meditation.

Recount their natures, tell which are

Virtuous like you, as well as fair.

Flore, Ceres and Pomona,
John Rea

As I FALL ASLEEP, I can see myself in a landscape from my childhood: on a clear lake in the Laurentian hills of Quebec, where there are no motor boats, only a small kayak gliding through sparkling sunlight that dances off the water's surface. The reflection is almost blinding. Sometimes I'm in the rocking kayak, other times I view this scene from a huge rock lifted out of the primordial waters back in the dawn of time. Then I find myself falling asleep in the warmth of the sun. I am safe.

I can get that feeling back when I stand in the garden on a warm summer evening and watch light fade into early evening. Small blobs of colour change before my eyes. First the reds, then the blues; then the yellows and whites glisten as though imbued with a magic dust. We are told that the eye loves novelty and will get used to anything, but I can never take this time of day for granted, nor the sight of my garden at one of its moments of perfection.

I UNDERSTAND WHY Chinese scholars would wait for their favourite tree peony to open, and sit for three days doing nothing else except meditate on the beauty of the blooms. There are days when I want to do nothing except gaze at a leaf or a blossom: the soft, watered silk of newly emerging peonies, or the near-black of the art deco leaves of the oak leaf hydrangea, *Hydrangea quercifolia*, or the delicate bells on the enkianthus. They can all be seen in paintings I've loved, but despite artistic genius, there is so much more soul to them in reality, in the garden.

I remember once sitting at the bottom of a hill looking up into a forest, and being amazed by the vast number of greens being flaunted as they changed with the nuance of the shifting light. I couldn't put a name to them all, but I knew each was different from the other. I could see the infinite variety in tone and hue.

As I've grown into gardening, none of the original enchantment has dissipated. But now I know that when the leaves of the ginkgo turn a glorious yellow, it is the carotenoids in the soil. The Japanese maple, in sharp contrast, is affected by anthocyanins. The maple's neon red causes the eyes to smart with its brief, intense moment of flaming glory. But when the leaves tumble down to make a velvet carpet on the ground beneath the low droop of its branches, my heart swells to the point of breaking.

THE AUTUMNAL GARDEN has the burnished air of a Cree summer. The first light frost has bitten off the heads of annuals, but the garden is intact, and it is captivating. Not quite decayed, but nicely decadent. The heat of autumn's colours make up for the cool air. What would life be like without all this? The garden is almost a mystical presence in my life. I cannot imagine doing without it.

These sights constantly enchant me. Of course, the fact that I might have had something to do with all this wonder and glory isn't lost on some part of me that wants to manipulate nature, to have control over it. The hummock shapes of low shrubs, with so many different colours of foliage, are my sculptures. They give me a wonderful feeling that something in my life has shape and form, even when all else is skidding out of control.

SCIENCE TELLS US that as the eye gathers in light, it can identify between 150 and 200 colours. Given the huge amount of pleasure colour gives us, it's strange to think that it doesn't actually exist. Colour itself is all light—electromagnetic radiation from the sun—and only some of this comes to us in the form of visible light. These light rays in turn are reflected back to the retina, which breaks down the rays into what we identify as colour. Any rays longer than red are invisible, and anything shorter than violet would be visible to bees but not to people.

GARDENERS KNOW the sky is our one constant—and it is never empty. We automatically look to it for weather reports as much as for sheer pleasure. The most glorious sunsets I've ever seen were on the Prairies, where I was born, or in Labrador, where we lived for many years. Yet as the city I now live in gets more and more filthy, the sunsets become more dazzling. Though I know part of its glory comes from the long red rays refracted by the prism of pollution hanging over the city, nothing dissipates the sense of joyous display. Ominous as this may be, I can't help relishing such a gorgeous sight—especially during our long, dismally grey winters.

WHAT PEOPLE RESPOND TO most readily in gardens are colours that are either completely harmonious with each other or strongly contrasting. Anything in between is somehow unsatisfying, and leaves the viewer with little response.

With the exception of the colour of certain blooms that attract bees, wasps or moths, or the protective coloration of some animals, we don't know what special purpose colours have. But we have applied our sense of beauty to them wholeheartedly.

We all have favourite colour schemes: Mine happens to be deep cobalt blue and yellow. Those shades remind me of the warmth of the winter sun in the south of France, and they give me comfort no matter where I find them (a tablecloth, a painting, the mug for my morning cup of coffee). When I apply this to my garden, I find it breathtakingly beautiful. Masses of blue *muscari* along with yellow daffodils rouse me to great activity outdoors. These are my signs of spring. Everyone has their own colour coding that can raise up their spirits or dampen their mood. Every colour has an enormous emotive quality, often connected to events from each individual's past.

Animals adapt their coloration to fit into the landscape or to attract the opposite sex. They can change the colour of their plumage over only a few generations if it's a matter of survival. But many animals are either blind to colour, or see colours that we can't. What is white to us, for instance, is blue to the bee.

The colours in the public gardens where I live are mostly a cacophony of strident oranges, yellows and harsh reds, along with magentas that feel like adolescents demanding attention.

They are designed by folks, it seems, who have never looked at nature in the raw.

You need only cast your eye toward the sides of roads that have not been mowed or drenched with poisons to keep out unwanted weeds (in other words, wild flowers). The misty ecru of Queen Anne's lace, the cobalt blue of chicory, pink and white mallows, golden mustards, grasses, the purple of wild asters and the beginnings of the deep lemon of solidago grow in an engaging jumble.

Here is untended harmony and delight, unweeded and watered only by nature. The plants tumble purposefully over the verge, so that there is a place for the butterflies and bugs that wander desperately through the suburbs looking for some place to land, let alone live.

The patterns of colour I find by the side of the road are mirrored in my garden, sometimes by serendipity, more often by design. I find comfort in this echoing of nature. There is no clashing, clanging or haranguing. Just a gentle mix of plants that seem to live quite happily together.

THE SKIN AND EYES absorb ultraviolet rays, which penetrate past our protective top layer of melanin. The sun is our lifeline to survival, and yet it has become a danger to us as well. As the ozone layer thins, we are becoming vulnerable to ultraviolet light. Elisabeth Sheldon is one of North America's finest garden writers, and one of the most fantastic gardeners I've ever met. She is also slowly losing her sight, apparently because she sunbathed indiscriminately and never wore sunglasses until she was forced to.

However, Sheldon has learned to identify everything in her garden by touch and smell, by feeling its roots. She recognizes every plant she has ever worked with or even seen long ago. Her garden demonstrates all the finest principles of harmony, with or without acute sight, because she knows about colour.

Elisabeth Sheldon's work is nothing short of phenomenal. The long, main beds in her garden contain a melange of soft pinks, blues, whites and silvers. As if this visual feast weren't enough, she then leads visitors through a shady green glade and throws open the gate of a small, enclosed space. This is her secret garden. Inside is an extraordinary revelation—a tumult of purples, reds, deep bronze, oranges and yellows radiantly working together with warmth and light. As her eyesight becomes dimmer, her own need for stronger colours has created one of the most dazzling garden sights I've seen anywhere.

COLOUR CAN CHANGE a mood. Harmonious colour creates a sense of unity, of serenity. It has the ability to slow down the body, stretch out the alpha waves and make us feel supremely relaxed. Pink is considered a passive, warm colour and therefore a calming one. In one study, patients looking at red lights became excited. In another, patients with tremors were calmed by looking at blue light. Green is another colour found to have a tranquillizing effect on those within its confines. There is always a "green room" in theatres or television studios, a place where actors get ready to go on stage or in front of the camera. And, of course, nature itself is filled with green, and is the most relaxing environment of all.

Hot colours such as scarlet and purple thrill us. Perhaps they are reminders of the blood pumping through our veins. Dark, dank colours (mud, dead leaves, threatening clouds) depress us, perhaps because they are the opposite of the bright colours that announce the vitality of life.

Colours that harmonize and hit the eye in a pleasing way have a pigment in common: yellow and green, for example, go well together because green contains yellow. Contrasting colours can be complementary, but they share nothing: yellow and blue, for instance. But because they are so dissimilar, each heightens the effect of the other. Perhaps this is why blue and yellow seem so filled with energy to me.

I certainly experienced the effect of colour in Elisabeth Sheldon's garden. The cool calm of her long border created a sense of tranquillity. To step into her brilliant secret garden was to be warmed to the core of my being. After I'd been sitting there for a while, I could feel my body stirring and becoming pleasurably excited. It was an intense experience, though, and eventually I wanted to move because of the midday light. Too hot. Glorious as the combinations were, and however much they pleased me aesthetically, my personal taste is for the more subdued. After a while, I needed a respite from the colours' strength. Even though I wanted to go back to the long, cool borders, however, I could understand having this contained plot of extraordinary colour as a place to go for reconstituting energy.

Sheldon's garden changed the way I look at colour. Intense colours jammed together make sense when one hue leads into the next with no jarring transition. Reds, oranges, purples, bronze and all the other hot colours advance toward the eye, making the plants larger, their hues more intense. Plants in these colours appear to have more solidity, more weight, and putting them together requires much care and a great colour sense. It's important to remember, too, that these stimulating colours look more brilliant at sunrise or sunset, while crisp colours like blue look their best at high noon.

As I was sitting among Sheldon's superb array of flowers so enchantingly put together, I couldn't help thinking about two other great gardeners whose eyesight failed: the English gardener Gertrude Jekyll, and the French Impressionist painter Claude Monet. Jekyll was a painter who turned to gardening as her eyes became increasingly feeble. Soil became her canvas, plants her palette, and she applied all the principles she'd learned through her watercolours to the point where, today, she is far better known for her gardening than she ever was for her art.

Monet used his garden at Giverny over and over again in his paintings during the 43 years he lived and gardened there. His is the supreme painterly garden, filled with rich red poppies, yellow marguerites and brilliant blue cornflowers. Even in his famous lily pond, he planted so that the light would catch certain plants at a specific angle. Then he painted every square inch in every possible light and time of day to show the infinite possibilities of light and colour. Distilled light. Nothing rare or unusual here in the choice of plants, just sheer genius at combining and rendering them. In fact, such was the infinite variety Monet found in nature, he painted variations on the lily pond from its installation in 1892 until his death in 1926.

What was it in the garden, what in their souls, that impelled these artists to work on so diligently, long past the time when failing vision might have branded them handicapped? The draw of light and colour—the healing garden.

$\mathcal{T}$OUCH

Touch fills our memory with a

detailed key as to how we're shaped.

A mirror would mean nothing

without touch....

A NATURAL HISTORY OF THE SENSES,
DIANE ACKERMAN

I FEEL I KNOW what Diane Ackerman is writing about
without even analyzing it. My garden makes me feel sensuous.
It reaches out and compels me to touch, to use my hands,
my fingers. I run them over the lacy achilleas, across the
silvery drift of stachys and pull them through a sweep of
golden grass. As I caress plants, my whole body feels more
vibrant and refreshed. I wander deeper into the garden,
deeper into my own thoughts.

I want to touch and taste and examine every leaf I
see here. Peppermint says something to me—something
refreshing. But it also has yellow in it, with such subtle
variegations that I reach into a clump and pull off a leaf to
pop into my mouth. It tastes of cool, green waters. The pale
velvet of the enchanting lady's mantle, *Alchemilla mollis*, holds
the last drop of dew at its centre for hours. Though I know it
will spread ruthlessly through the garden the minute
I turn my back, still I am beckoned to stroke its velvet leaves.

Not to feel a garden, not to touch it constantly, would be
to miss a good deal of its charm. And it is this quality that
makes it a place of such importance for older people, and
those who are isolated or sick. Who will hug and kiss them at
any time of the day if they are alone? Not being touched, we
lose the sense of touching and we lose part of our humanity.
With a garden close by, the need to make physical contact is
always satisfied.

Most of the studies in horticultural therapy emphasize the need to touch plants, feel soil, run fingers through water. To make contact with what's natural. This forms a connectedness with what we know from the past. For the elderly, being able to choose what colour of plants to grow, to handle them on a daily basis, gives them a sense of worth and value. It also awakens in them their own creativity by making these choices.

For children, feeling a plant is terribly important. Kids love to touch water and they'll squish anything you give them. Studies at the New York Botanical Garden showed that not only do children love to plant, to weed and to harvest, they also love to "interact with topiaries, crawl through plant-laden tunnels, climb bridges and hide behind maze walls." Gardens are fantasies for children; they don't have to know where a path goes as long as they can use their imaginations.

Horticultural therapy has also unearthed the fact that patients who raked leaves or made a compost—in other words, accomplished some kind of physical work in the garden—reached endorphin highs similar to those produced by jogging or bicycling. Most people aren't aware that they are actually involved in aerobic exercise when they garden, but they know they feel much better each time they do some physical labour.

SINCE ALL ANIMALS respond to touch, what about plants themselves? Touch in a human sets off sensors in the brain. Does it do the same in plants? If we touch them with affection or hate, do they understand? Scientists have conducted experiments in which a group of plants was set up in a room and wired to measure their electrical response to their environment. A person came in, trashed half of the plants and left abruptly. When the same person entered the room afterward, the remaining plants gave off such strong signals, the reaction could only be analogous to fear.

WHEN I TOUCH a plant's roots, I feel as though I am getting to know it. I like to stroke the leaves as I put plants into the garden, so that I can try to put one next to another that may feel very different. I don't look at any plant, even in isolation, without wanting to know something about its relationships with every other plant and to me, and part of getting to know someone or something is by touch.

Gardening has taught me much about my own sensuality. My garden begs to be embraced as I myself like to be embraced. And if I lived alone, I would still have this very sensual companion.

Sound

As I listen from a beach-chair in the shade

To all the noises that my garden made,

It seemed to me only proper that words

Should be withheld from vegetables and birds.

A robin with no Christian name ran through

The Robin Anthem which was all it knew,

And rustling flowers for some third party waited

To say which pairs, if any, should get mated.

Their Lonely Betters,
W. H. Auden

From the very beginning, sound has been significant in gardening. The first Persian gardens always had murmuring water in them. Water is the touchstone of all life. It is the symbol of birth; without it we die. We are inexorably drawn to oases in the desert, rushing waterfalls, the edge of the sea—the sound of water, wherever it can be found.

We've turned much of this Earth into such a noisy place. We can easily become sick with the incessant pounding, drilling and buzzing that surround us, particularly in cities. The garden should be a place of some quiet to work its healing magic.

Anyone who has travelled to Europe has experienced the sudden calm of an inner courtyard in the midst of a bustling city: a few plants, a dribbling tap or a piazza with a huge fountain that serves as a place to gather.

I FEEL I ALSO UNDERSTAND the profound meaning of sound when I hold my grandson and sing softly to him. He croons back at me as if to echo this extraordinary instant of communication. So slight a moment, and yet for the two of us, something that will bind us for life and a memory that will last me forever. Whenever I hear a cooing sound, whether it comes from a human or animal throat, I am reminded of him and times like these.

THE GARDEN HAS ITS own voice: The whispers of shrubs rubbing against each other, the slight hiss of insects, the babble of a fountain or murmur of water sliding across rocks becomes a balm for the sagging, weary soul. The sound of wind rustling through the leaves of grass becomes one of the songs of winter.

Almost everything that surrounds us makes some kind of noise, from the wind moving through wheat to the tinkling of the wind chimes hanging outside the window to heavy-laden branches scraping against each other. These are the sounds of both the animation and the solidity of nature. Each one evokes memories reaching back into childhood. By listening to nature we are also reconnecting with ourselves.

Birdsongs make us feel free to soar as they can. This is one of the reasons that new hospital gardens or those for elderly patients have an atrium with birds, which cheer up patients extraordinarily. Remember how buoyant you feel when you wake to the sound of birds singing in the trees.

Think how this might affect someone who couldn't get out of bed. Their sounds remind us that, fragile though life is, joy is possible no matter what.

The healing garden includes insects. There's no getting away from the fact that a healthy garden will be filled with buzzing. This actually has proven to be another successful form of distraction in hospital gardens—once again, luring the patient away from self in the contemplation of these small creatures' lives. We could not survive without the work they do. Sound reminds us of different perspectives.

SOUND TRAVELS AT 1,100 feet per second. It is the movement of molecules sent trembling all around the source—whether it's the flapping of a bird's wings or the whir of an insect. These molecules hit the ear and set the eardrum vibrating, the three bones (hammer, anvil and stirrup) press the inner ear fluid and that tells the brain what we're hearing. The greater the frequency, the higher the pitch.

Bats send out sonar impulses that bounce off anything in front of them and the echoes come back, telling them what's ahead. A moth can hear a bat coming because it has such an accurate and sensitive system that it can pick up the bat's sonar noise even in dense shrubbery. It jams the bat's frequency by making a sound wave itself, which messes up the bat's radar and enables the moth to escape, for the moment, the bat's voracious appetite.

Bees are also no slouches in the noise department. Their wings beat at 160 cycles per second, making a sound of E below middle C. This produces a horrendous rumbling noise to any smaller creatures. If we could actually hear all the creatures—the sap pumping through plants' vascular systems, the munching and chewing of thousands of insects in the garden, the high-pitched noises of bats and moths—we would never be able to experience a still night. It would be as bad as hearing all the blips and gurgles of our own bodies.

MUSIC CAN DRIVE US to great depths of grief or make a heart almost burst with joy. Life would be devastatingly empty without the sound of wind rushing through the trees. But water adds something else. Water soothes the ragged edges of life.

In Japanese gardens, plants aren't emphasized as much as the ambience—cool mosses, stepping stones for a slow stroll where you can gaze at the ferns growing nearby. And every garden must have the sound of water in some form. What is, after all, more conducive to meditation than water? Some aquatic element is to be found in almost every Japanese garden, whether it's the sound of a gentle, constant drip or a bowl of water to reflect sun and moonlight.

Sound, especially the sound of water running over stones, may take a Japanese gardener many years to fully comprehend. Each tone has meaning and is an inducement to wisdom.

We in the West are not so precise. The water I have is a simple fountain that bubbles away in an old hammered-tin tub. It softens everything around when I turn it on. My grandson spends ages (for him) holding his hand in the water, moving it around, watching curiously to see how the sun falls on the drops. He's been fascinated with it since he could barely stand, and that absorption has never ceased. Will this sound bring back memories of being at our house and recall the things we do? I expect it will.

Like scents, the sound of water can bring back the past. I recollect a stream that used to run through our property when I was a child. It was spanned by a rickety bridge and was on the way to the best picnic spot in the world—a grassy hill strewn with boulders.

I used to play in the stream, build dams to make the water noisier, try to catch guppies and cool off in the shade of the trees. Both the way there and the way back demanded a stop. When I hear that tone now in any running water, I can taste the sandwiches (peanut butter and banana) and the little bottle of milk (chocolate). I can hear the noise of the countryside: a tractor, the scream of a hawk, a distant dog barking.

In the city, using some kind of water to mask the surrounding noise is essential. It can be done easily, with a container and a circulating pump with a fountain fixture. The smallest space, even a window, can accommodate this assemblage. I'm often tempted to set up my little fountain in the house when I badly need the sound of water in winter, cut off too long from working in the garden. The water returns me to summer enchantment. It is also cleaning the air, making it more moist and spreading negative ions to perk up drooping spirits. Healing, in other words.

The water in the garden not only adds sound, it also attracts bugs and birds to come and feed when the pump is turned off, which I do regularly for their benefit. The birds are safe now that we no longer have a cat, and the fountain keeps them close at all times. Water also draws light into the garden: sunlight and moonlight. I use mirrors near my water just to add to the illusion of space, but it's the water that creates the real mystery.

A country pond, of course, has a different value. It reflects the sky, compresses space and becomes a home for all sorts of plants and animals. But even without vast outdoor expanses, it's possible to create the illusion of space when you work with water.

Diane Ackerman writes that "the word 'poet' comes from an Aramaic word that denotes the sound of water flowing over pebbles."

Water can be the focus of attention, compelling us to use our imaginations, to be contemplative. But best of all, water is good for dreaming—about the past, into the future.

THE WIND SOUGHING through the trees can be a comfort. It cools and moistens and acts as an air conditioner for the whole garden. I hear the wind on some nights and I am back lying beside a field of wheat, feeling I was part of all creation and the universe.

My fantasy life always includes being by the ocean and listening to the relaxing sound of water. It makes me feel as though I am floating. Calm. This is probably true for most people who have ever been close to the sea and heard its rhythms.

As a child, however, I lived in the far north. The two-metre-deep ice breaking up and the ice floes grinding against one other made such terrifying noises that I would quake in real apprehension, imagining this was the end of the world. Every so often, the midnight sound of a motor shifting gears, a train rumbling past or a sharp retort of the wind in the trees will bring back this frightening memory, and I am a child again, alone in the dark.

My grandson Nick is in love with the sound of his own voice. He can spend huge amounts of time rhyming words. New words tumble out, invented words, and I understand once again why it is that children respond to poetry before any other organized form of language. Studies have shown that exposing little kids to constant loud noises makes them more aggressive, leading to disagreeable or antisocial behaviour. Perhaps we can forgive children who grow up in noisy cities, bereft of greenery, if we understand what is happening to them sensually. We can give them parks in school yards instead of concrete. We can let them dig in the dirt.

RIGHT: *This reflecting pond both calms the mind and provides habitat for insects and animals.* (PHOTOGRAPH BY PADDY WALES IN THE GARDEN OF GLEN PATTERSON)

OVERLEAF: *A small part in my own garden, where I like to sit and absorb the scents of early evening.* (PHOTOGRAPH BY MARJORIE HARRIS)

How to Design a Healing Garden

The healing garden can be a bench under a tree near a border of flowers, a small pot lovingly tended on a window sill or vast acres. Each requires a different kind of involvement, and yet each is the same. It is the giving up of one's self to nature. If a mere picture of a natural setting can give us comfort, then what a gift it is to be able to poke fingers into the soil, even if only for a few minutes a day. It satisfies a primitive part of our being, and if we suppress it too long, we get sick or go mad.

MY HEALING GARDEN

A healing garden needs little more than plants, some sunlight and lots of love. In my own garden, the balm of my life,

I grow hundreds of plants and scatter herbs throughout,
mixing them with all kinds of other plants that might have
the same needs they do.

I've also placed two benches in strategic spots so they
are in the shade at special times of the day. They both have
a splendid view over that particular section of the garden.
Sitting there at any time, scents drift out over the garden, and
I can reach out and touch plants close by.

It's a good idea to establish a few guiding principles
whenever you bring plants into your life. I like using repeated
patterns of colour (in my case, soft greys) everywhere:
lavenders, artemisias and helichrysum. Their scents are also
complementary: a bit tart, almost like a cold splash of water
on the face. They make you feel more perky.

If I had the space and lots of sun, I'd make a special
formal herb garden, but unfortunately my garden doesn't
allow me to do it. However, what follows is a list of all kinds
of plants I can't live without, which in most cases aren't
mentioned elsewhere in this book:

❧ *Salvia officinalis*: You need go no further than the
  common, everyday sage. It's such a glorious, blowzy plant.

Chapter Six

It won't last forever, it might be hit with winterkill, but its scent, texture and blue-grey leaves make it very satisfying.

❧ *Lavandula angustifolia,* English lavender: What a magnificent plant. I use it in potpourris, to freshen up closets and keep out moths, and mix it with dried flowers all the time. It's the most forgiving of plants, will grow anywhere and if it seems to die back in the winter, just whack it down to about 2 in. from the ground and watch it come back again. No wonder it's an encouraging plant for the sick.

❧ *Allium sativum,* garlic: An absolute necessity in every garden. Allicin, the odour emitted by the roots, destroys bacteria on other plants. Garlic is also an excellent antiseptic, used in food, ground up and applied to the body or rubbed on the soles of the feet. To grow garlic, I use large cloves, preferably from an organically grown head of red garlic, and plant them at least 1.5 in. deep and about 5 in. apart in full sun. I try to get them in a few weeks before hard frost sets in. When the little flower heads appear the following year, bend over the stems, including the flowers, and let them die down so you can harvest in the fall.

Normally I scatter them all over the garden where I think they'll be useful: next to roses to keep out fungal diseases or near other plants such as tomatoes as a heal-all.

❧ *Thymus*: There are dozens and dozens of thymes. Get them all, and use them in patterns to make a foliage tapestry. Some bloom, all have magnificent scent.

Those are the basics, and you need little else. But with more space, all of these could go into a healing garden:

❧ *Calamintha nepeta* has clusters of pale blue flowers. In my garden it grows in a dreadful spot—a lot of competition, not a lot of sun and neglect—but it thrives.

❧ *Caulophyllum thalictroides*, blue cohosh, is a native plant mentioned in every herbal, and to watch the strange, stiff, purple leaves emerge in the woodland in spring is to understand why. It looks magical. Cohosh is an Algonquin word, and they used it to treat rheumatism and arthritis. I like the delicate tracery of its leaves.

❧ *Centaurea cyanus*, bachelor's buttons, fill in empty places like no other plant with their gorgeous, deep blue flowers. They dry very nicely, too.

❧ *Chamaemelum nobile*, chamomile, a low-growing plant that tucks in almost anywhere and releases its scent when walked on. Excellent near a path.

❧ *Cimicifuga racemosa*, black snakeroot, is a strange woodland plant. It has slightly scented, bottle-brush spikes of flowers over large, fern-like leaves and blooms from August on.

❧ *Echinacea purpurea*, purple coneflower, has a rough, rather wild quality to it that can be softened with the downy velvet of lamb's ears, *Stachys lanata*. Echinacea is now considered one of the best ways to ward off colds.

❧ *Eupatorium purpureum*, Joe-Pye-weed, has huge, almost ghost-like heads that bees love. It grows wild by the side of the road, but the domestic version is even more enormous.

❧ *Hepatica nobilis*, liverwort, isn't a tonic for the liver, as we used to believe, but it is an invaluable shade plant.

❧ *Hydrastis*, goldenseal, is a lovely plant that, like echinacea, has reached legendary status in the health-food stores. Big green leaves with tiny red fruits.

❧ *Hyssopus officinalis*, hyssop, is used in my garden not just for its deep blue flowers and eerie scent, but also as an edger around a formal border. Two other herbs work as

edgers just as well: *Santolina chamaecyparissus* and
Artemisia camphorata.

❧ *Myrrhis odorata*, sweet cicely, has huge, fern-like leaves
that grow well in cool shade. It also has an almost anise-
like scent. The black seeds are edible, tasting a bit like
licorice, and are often used as a low-calorie sweetener.

❧ *Nepeta grandiflora*, catmint, will have blooms for as long
as two months. Even though you can't eat it, brew it or
cut it, the blue blooms are essential.

I think the most important aspect of my garden in
keeping me balanced is that, although I have many ambitions
for it, I don't let them get in the way of the pure enjoyment of
being in the garden. It isn't work, it's beyond play. What I do
there is the most selfish part of my life. I do it for me.

A GARDEN OF POTS

Containers are an extremely satisfying way to garden. Anyone
can grow herbs and exquisite ornamentals together in one
little pot on a window sill. All the better if there is a small
balcony with some sun. Size doesn't matter in the healing

garden; what does count is being part of it—tending to it and looking carefully at what you are growing.

Most herbs and vegetables prefer about six hours of sunbathing a day, but they can get along on fewer. A decent transplanting trowel, longer than an ordinary trowel and with a deep dish, will be useful. It makes it easier to get around the edges of plants and to squeeze bulbs into small spaces.

The kind of container really doesn't matter. I've seen glorious herb, flower and vegetable gardens in wooden bushel baskets lined with plastic (with holes poked in it for drainage) or, as they do in Mediterranean countries, old olive-oil tins.

The nice thing about pots, or any container for that matter, is that you can move them around constantly. They will attract few bugs and never slugs, which is an improved form of gardening as far as I'm concerned. Few, if any, diseases attack pots, and they will be cosseted and warm because of their height. No digging, no backbreaking work and, with the right mix, a miniature landscape of wonderful plants at your fingertips.

Herbs fit into containers of any size. They are such an uncomplaining lot that you can change your mind and make new mixes at your whim. You can easily carry or drag them around a garden from sun spot to sun spot, making them a movable palette. Putting a pot on a dolly will make it easy to move around where needed. And it's possible to corral all the great invasive plants, such as mints, in a container.

They require a bit of care, but that's the whole point of a healing garden—by caring for the plants, you are also caring for yourself. It doesn't matter what kinds of plants catch your fancy—a few pots of sweet tomatoes or a mass of pansies. It's the doing of it, the companionship of a plant, that heals.

THE THERAPEUTIC GARDEN

Mitchell Hewson, the horticultural therapist at Guelph's Homewood Health Care Centre, has developed, through a great deal of ingenuity, a healing garden with raised beds. Unlike the more usual concept, however, his consist of movable racks of pots that are easy to roll into position for someone in a wheelchair. Pots can be rearranged for both wheelchairs and the sun, whichever is needed. Hewson works indoors with his patients during the winter, and recommends the following ironclad plants. All are non-poisonous and easy to care for:

For warm conditions:

❧ Dwarf orange tree provides fragrance plus lovely blooms and bright orange fruit. It needs really good drainage, and should be kept moist but not over-watered. It also needs sun, heat and lots of fertilizing. The container should be 15 in. in diameter to hold this little tree.

❧ *Hibiscus rosa-sinensis*, Chinese hibiscus, has huge tropical blooms. It needs the same treatment as above.

❧ *Coleus*: Its brightly coloured leaves are maintained by pinching out the little flower buds. It requires indirect light but not too much shade, or the leaves will lose their intensity.

For cooler conditions:

❧ Ferns, begonias, and *Tradescantia virginiana* are all good plants for shade. Cut back regularly and make new plants.

For northern light:

❧ *Philodendron*; Peace lily, *Spathiphyllum;* and corn plant, *Dracaena*: Keep the soil moist but not soggy. All these plants love warmth and light, although the last will take quite a lot of shade as well.

See bibliography to contact Mr. Hewson.

THE TACTILE GARDEN

A touching garden can be a wonderfully satisfying theme, both physically and emotionally. All the words that describe the most magnificent fabrics—such as silk and velvet—apply here. These are the most aromatic of all the herbs. To touch is to smell:

- Lavender; sage; mint (keep it in pots—this plant is tremendously invasive); garlic chives, *Allium tuberosum*; lemon balm, *Melissa officinalis*; any of the dozens of thymes; and the ferny yarrows; and *Galium odoratum*, sweet woodruff.

- The culinary herbs: All of them—basil, chervil, dill, rosemary, marjoram, oregano and parsley—have sensual qualities, and they will add immeasurably to flavour in cooking.

- Herbs will give their best qualities if they are harvested in midmorning, just before the plant's flowers open and when essential oils are at their most pungent.

- Inevitably, pets and pests invade the garden. Plants in the *Compositae*, daisy, family—such as tansy, feverfew and fleabane—have pest-repellent qualities. Plant them near the plants you particularly value and perhaps both pets and pests will clear off.

❧ Marigolds have become famous as a companion plant because they excrete a pesticide from their roots that affects such things as eel worms in tomatoes or potatoes. North American Indians knew that pyrethrum, *Tanacetum coccineum,* was a pesticide hundreds of years ago.

❧ Among other invaluable touch-me kinds of plants are lamb's ears, *Stachys lanata,* which have velvety grey leaves.

In the long view, of course, all plants are touchable, with rare exceptions such as rue, *Ruta graveolens,* and euphorbias, both of which make some people break out in a rash.

The Contemplative Garden

There are many principles involved in creating a contemplative garden, but the most important requirement is a cool glade, usually in the shade, with plenty of ferns, hostas and other woodland plants.

❧ Have a central focus. Any object, fountain, water feature or even plant will aid a person meditating in the garden.

❧ The sound of water is very important to contemplation.

Sound is difficult to orchestrate, so be careful to make sure the sound is pleasing rather than demanding (too loud, too much splash). The idea is to focus the mind, which means a water feature that you can look at (pond, moon bowl) and that softens the intrusion of the outside world. I find a simple self-circulating fountain pump is cheap and works very well.

❧ Paths are very important to enable you to stroll through this kind of garden. They often curve, so there is always something to draw the viewer forward, toward a place to sit, perhaps, or a shady bower. In some contemplative gardens, stones are deliberately placed so that only one person can walk on them and only slowly. In this way you are forced to change your normal hectic pace, and take time to appreciate each plant in its proper place.

❧ A secluded corner where the scent of herbs can waft over a bench that offers a view of the rest of the garden is the ideal place to sit and meditate.

❧ Soft colours will soothe the tattered edges of the soul. Use a palette that includes a lot of white and silver to tone down all the other colours.

A GARDEN OF THERAPY

Twyla Rusnak is a landscape designer in Victoria, B.C., who has worked on gardens for the elderly and, most recently, for Alzheimer patients. She has some good advice for creating a garden with this in mind.

- ❧ Alzheimer patients must feel they are travelling without being trapped—but they can't be allowed to wander off either. Rusnak designed looping pathways that may lead to dead ends (fences) but then go off in another, enticing direction. The gates and the fences are designed with trellis with openings 5 in. wide, to give a feeling of airiness but also of safety.

- ❧ It sometimes helps to include an object that triggers strong memories. In one garden, they brought in a 1962 car (without the engine) as a place for patients to sit. It's parked among the vegetation and provides a little privacy for daydreaming and perhaps recalling the past.

- ❧ She also uses vines, enclosed aviaries or a pool to remind patients of earlier days or gardens.

A few other good principles Ms. Rusnak follows:

❧ Allow the patients to choose the annuals—they take great pleasure in this.

❧ Keep dark, dank plantings at the periphery of a garden so they won't present anything formidable.

❧ Install plants that reach about waist height. This makes them easy to reach and touch, but doesn't cut off the patients' ability to keep their bearings—using a tree or a gazebo. She makes sure there are cues all through the garden.

❧ The garden should be at the same grade as the building, so that it's easy to enter it.

❧ Covered walkways, benches and bird baths are all reasons to draw patients into the garden.

BY APPROACHING PLANTS as part of the health of our own bodies and spirits, not as a mere hobby or a way to fill in time, we can continue on refreshed in our own journey through life, connected to our own past and our present. Plants heal, gardens heal, nature heals. It's absolutely necessary to value them highly for what they can do for us, and to treat them with the respect they deserve. To learn how to respect and love ourselves, we have no further to go than the garden.

Suggested Reading

Ackerman, Diane. *A Natural History of the Senses*. New York: Vintage, 1991.

Berry, Thomas. *The Dream of the Earth*. San Francisco: Sierra Club Books, 1988.

Bodanis, David. *The Secret Garden: Dawn to Dusk in the Astonishing Hidden World of the Garden*. London: Simon & Schuster, 1992.

Brown, Deni. *Encyclopedia of Herbs & Their Uses*. Montreal: Reader's Digest Association, 1995.

Castleman, Michael. *The Healing Herbs*. Emmaus, PA: Rodale Press, 1991.

Clarke, Ethne. *Herb Garden Design*. New York: Macmillan, 1995.

Fox, Matthew. *Original Blessing*. Santa Fe: Bear & Co., 1984.

Densmore, Frances. *How Indians Use Wild Plants*. New York: Dover Publications Inc., 1974.

Garland, Sarah. *The Herb Garden*. New York: Viking, 1984.

Hewson, Mitchell L. *Horticulture as Therapy*. HTM, 150 Delhi St., Guelph, Ont. N1E 6K9, 1994.

Hobhouse, Penelope. *Gardening Through the Ages*. New York: Simon & Schuster, 1992.

Hobhouse, Penelope. *Colour in Your Garden*. London: Collins, 1984.

Keville, Kathi. *Herbs: An Illustrated Encyclopedia*. New York: Friedman/Fairfax, 1994.

Lopez, Barry. *Arctic Dreams*. New York: Bantam, 1987.

McKibben, Bill. *The End of Nature*. New York: Anchor Books, 1989.

Lovelock, James. *The Ages of Gaia*. New York: Norton, 1988.

Loewer, Peter. *The Evening Garden*. New York: Macmillan, 1993.

Minter, Sue. *The Healing Garden*. London: Headline, 1995.

Plotkin, Mark J. *Tales of a Shaman's Apprentice*. New York: Penguin, 1993.

Reader's Digest. *Magic and Medicine of Plants*. Montreal: Reader's Digest Association, 1986.

Relf, Diane, ed. *The Role of Horticulture in Human Well-Being and Social Development: A National Symposium*. Portland, OR: Timber Press, 1992.

Squire, David. *Color in Your Garden*. Emmaus, PA: Rodale Press, 1991.

Weiner, Michael. *Earth Medicine—Earth Foods*. New York: Collier Books, 1972.

Wilder, Louise Beebe. *The Fragrant Garden*. New York: Dover, 1974 (republication of *The Fragrant Path*; Macmillan, 1932).

PAPERS

Walk, Brian J., Marianne B. Karsh and Nik Ansell. "Trees, Forestry, and the Responsiveness of Creation." *Cross Current*, Summer 1994.

Cox, Paul Alan, and Michael J. Balic. "The Ethnobotanical Approach to Drug Discovery." *Scientific American*, June 1994.